3

But Snakebite had a friend
named Jimmy Raven.
Every day, Jimmy went out
with bread and apples.

Snakebite came running.
Snort! Snort! Munch! Munch!

Jimmy Raven said,
"You're not mean.
You're just very smart."

Snakebite

Story by Joy Cowley

Illustrations by Stephen Marchesi

Snakebite was a wild horse.
When the cowboys tried to rope him,
Snakebite would buck
and kick and bite.

The cowboys said to their boss,
"That Snakebite is plain old mean!"

One day, the boss said,
"Snakebite's going in the rodeo.
I will win the prize money,
because no one can stay
on his back."

Snakebite did not want
to go to the rodeo.

"I will come with you,"
said Jimmy Raven.

At the rodeo, three strong cowboys
wanted to ride Snakebite.

The first cowboy got on.
The gate opened,
and out came Snakebite,
bucking and kicking.

Down went the first cowboy.

8

9

It was the second cowboy's turn.
Snakebite jumped high in the air.
The cowboy fell in the dust,
and Snakebite bit him
on the seat of his pants.

The third cowboy did no better.
He tried to hold on,
but Snakebite bucked,
and the cowboy went
head over heels.

"That sure is a mean horse,"
everyone said.

"No! He's not mean!"
shouted Jimmy Raven.

Jimmy ran into the ring.
He talked to Snakebite
and patted his neck.
Then he climbed up
on the horse's back,
and they trotted around the ring.

The people cheered.
"The kid wins!" they said.

"Please, sir," said Jimmy to the boss.
"You can have the prize money
  if I can have Snakebite."

"It's a deal!" the boss said.

  Jimmy Raven smiled.
"Snakebite's not mean," he said.
"He's just very smart."